THE STORY OF TWO GARDENS

Quran Stories for Little Hearts

By

SANIYASNAIN KHAN

www.goodwordbooks.com

Long long ago, there lived two friends. One of them was a rich gardener, while the other one was a poor farmer. The gardener owned a huge plot of land.

2

He cultivated his land very ably and developed it into two beautiful and blooming gardens. They were full of flowers and all kind of fruits, especially grapes and dates. The vineyards were set about with palm trees and watered by a running stream.

5

Whenever the gardener would visit his gardens, he would be thrilled by seeing trees laden with ripe fruits. His heart would be filled with pride and arrogance

He would think this was all a result of his hard work and clever planning. He would ignore the fact that his entire fortune was actually a blessing from Allah. Without Allah's help, no one can achieve a single thing on this earth.

One day his friend, the poor farmer visited him. The gardener took him around his beautiful garden and proudly said to him, "I am richer than you and my clan is mightier than yours." Looking at his gardens, he continued: "Surely this will never perish!" Puffed up with the evil of wealth he went on denying the Day of Judgement: "Nor do I believe that the hour of Doom will ever come."

Then he added: "Even if I return to my Lord, I shall surely find a better place than this." Little did he realize that all this was wishful thinking.

When the poor farmer noticed that his friend was behaving in a wicked way, he tried to correct him. He added: "Have you no faith in Him who created you from dust, from a little germ , and fashioned you into a man?" The poor man went on : "As for myself, Allah is my Lord, and I will associate no one else with Him."

He advised the gardener that instead of entering the garden proudly, he should have gone into it in all humility and should have said: "What Allah has ordained must surely come to pass: there is no strength except in Allah."

"Though you see me poorer than yourself and blessed with fewer children," the farmer argued, "yet my Lord may give me a garden better than yours, and send down thunder bolts from heaven upon your vineyards, turning them into a barren waste, or drain their water deep down into the earth, so that you will get no benefit from it."

The very next day was struck by calamity. All the fruits were destroyed. The gardener wrung his hands with grief at all that he had spent on them, for the vines had tumbled down upon their trellises.

On seeing this he realised his mistake and cried, "Would that I had served no other gods besides my Lord!"

23

This story is meant to teach believers never to speak proudly, but to say in all humility, "Whatever Allah has ordained must surely come to pass: there is no power save with Allah."

Find Out More

To know more about the message and meaning of Allah's words, look up the following parts of the Quran which tell the story of the two gardens.

Surah al-Kahf 18:32-42

24